HOW DO YOU WANT TO SHOW UP?

WORKBOOK

HOW DO YOU WANT TO SHOW UP?

Find Your Inner Truths—and Lead with Them

WORKBOOK

MELISSA WILLIAMS-GURIAN

Published by Melissa Williams-Gurian, Seattle
www.melissawilliamsgurian.com

Edited and Designed by Girl Friday Productions
www.girlfridayproductions.com

Editorial: Leslie Miller
Interior Design: Rachel Marek
Author photo © 2013 Ingrid Pape-Sheldon Photography

ISBN (Workbook): 978-0-9989051-3-6
e-ISBN (Workbook): 978-0-9989051-5-0

CONTENTS

What is it you really believe?
What is it you really want?
What is it you are here to do?

Did you start your career knowing answers to these questions but have drifted off course? Maybe you never stopped to consider these questions in the first place. No matter how talented we are, when we don't take the time to know ourselves and have those conversations, we don't work to our full capacity. This workbook takes you through an investigation of these questions and helps you answer the most important one:

How do you want to show up?

Leadership isn't just an attitude or a natural ability, it requires intentionality. Because intentions are invisible, every leader needs to understand how they are showing up—a process of looking inward and also extending outward.

How do you want to show up? What is your inner truth? What conversations do you need to have in order to show up with intention?

THE ELEPHANT IN THE ROOM

ARE YOU UNCLEAR ON WHAT YOU REALLY WANT, OR ARE YOU ABLE TO CLEARLY STATE YOUR NEEDS AND DESIRES?

DO YOU AVOID DELIVERING HARD FEEDBACK, OR ARE YOU ABLE TO SIT WITH THE DISCOMFORT OF OTHERS?

ARE YOU STUCK IN A CYCLE OF DISFUNCTION, OR ARE YOU ABLE TO MOVE THROUGH TO TAKE CORRECTIVE STEPS?

If everyone could show up and state their truths, needs, and desires at any given moment, learn to sit with others' discomfort, and then move to action, we would all create our best selves.

Alex's team could not love and respect him more. They think he is brilliant, encouraging, and motivating. His one fault? His relationship with his boss, John. John is, to put it bluntly, a jerk. He's charismatic as well, but his managerial approach is domineering, aggressive, and prone to attack. Alex feels it, of course. It's so bad he's ready to leave the company. But he's never told John how he feels. What Alex isn't owning up to is that John's behavior affects the whole company. After interactions with John, Alex's team finds their usually calm boss irritable and short.

What conversation should you be having that you're not having *right now*?

This could be with a colleague, friend or maybe with your boss. It shouldn't be hard to come up with—it's probably sitting right under the surface. Describe the problem behavior. How long has it been going on? What are the effects that you know about? Do you think the problem is affecting others around you as well? How?

A 2013 Stanford Business School survey found the highest area of concern regarding personal development for CEOs was learning skills for conflict management.

One of the most difficult things for all of us, including leaders, is sitting with the discomfort that hard conversations elicit in the other party. Even if a conversation is done well, the other party will experience and express negative emotions. They could include anger, sadness, tears, silence, defensiveness. We must all work continuously to learn to sit with those emotions when they come up and not back down, terminate the conversation, or try to "fix" them in other ways.

Imagine giving an employee a difficult performance review or telling a friend or family member a hard truth.

How do you imagine they would react? What would you do in response if they showed distress, anger, or sadness?

_____

_____

_____

_____

_____

_____

_____

_____

_____

_____

_____

_____

_____

_____

_____

_____

_____

_____

_____

_____

_____

_____

_____

CONVERSATION

In every conversation, we manage three parts

OURSELVES
Think
Feel
Want

THE MESSAGE
Intent
Body language
Tone

THEM
(in regard to what we said)
Think
Feel
Want

Effective communication starts with understanding that in every conversation, there is MY POINT OF VIEW (MY TRUTH) and THEIR POINT OF VIEW (THEIR TRUTH). Many difficult conversations get hung up on each party insisting their truth is the ABSOLUTE TRUTH, when in fact, that rarely exists.

What do feelings have to do with business? Everything! Whether we acknowledge it or not, our feelings dictate our behavior, and our behavior and communication have everything to do with productivity, company culture, and our success.

Think about the problem you described earlier and briefly summarize it below.

Now, look at the Feelings Chart. Circle all of the feelings you experience as a result of this problem.

_____

_____

_____

_____

_____

_____

_____

_____

FEELINGS CHART

INTENSITY OF FEELINGS	GLAD	SAD	MAD	AFRAID	ASHAMED
HIGH	Elated Excited Overjoyed Thrilled Exuberant Ecstatic Fired Up Delighted	Depressed Disappointed Alone Hurt Dejected Hopeless Sorrowful Miserable	Furious Enraged Outraged Aggravated Irate Seething	Terrified Horrified Scared Stiff Petrified Fearful Panicky	Sorrowful Remorseful Unworthy Worthless Disgraced Dishonored
MEDIUM	Cheerful Up Good Relieved Satisfied	Heartbroken Down Upset Distressed Regretful Melancholy	Upset Mad Hot Frustrated Agitated Disgusted	Scared Frightened Threatened Insecure Uneasy Shocked	Apologetic Defamed Sneaky Guilty
MILD	Content Pleasant Pleased	Unhappy Blue Lost Bad Dissatisfied	Perturbed Annoyed Uptight Put Out Irritated Touchy	Apprehensive Nervous Worried Timid Unsure Anxious	Embarrassed Disappointed Let Down

Look at the words you circled and use them to describe YOUR TRUTH about the situation.

Stay focused on what you know and what you feel. Don't make assumptions about the motivations of the other party. If I took my side fully, what would I say?

_____

_____

_____

_____

_____

_____

_____

_____

_____

_____

_____

_____

_____

_____

_____

_____

_____

_____

_____

_____

_____

_____

_____

_____

_____

_____

_____

_____

Now imagine taking *their* side fully. What would they say?

Being able to fully embody your truth, to get clear on why something is so important to you, and to understand your boundaries is an important skill set. Equally important is the work of building empathy. Productive and collaborative conversations stem from being able to fully imagine what the other thinks and feels.

How Are You Avoiding Difficult Conversations?

Alex thought that he was simply "taking" John's abuse and absorbing it, but that's almost never the case. Like most of us, Alex needed to put those negative feelings and emotions somewhere. We already know he expressed them to his team in the form of being short and rude with them following his interactions with John. But he also expressed them indirectly as well. In Alex's case, it took the form of missing deadlines and withholding information from his boss. Alex didn't recognize that while he was doing it, but after investigating how he felt after interactions with John, he realized he was trying to express to his boss, INDIRECTLY, how he felt about not being recognized for his worth and value.

Every step you can take toward addressing what is true for you directly, rather than indirectly, helps you gain power and self-confidence.

You probably recognize the term "passive-aggressive." When someone is passive-aggressive, they are expressing their emotions indirectly. While you avoid a difficult conversation, expressing your emotions in this way only takes more of your power away.

Go back to the problem you described and look at the feelings you said it elicits in you.

If you are honest with yourself, how are you *indirectly* expressing those feelings? What are the effects on the people around you? On your work? On your personal life?

How Our Family of Origin Affects Who We Are Now

The families we grew up with are with us long after we've gone out on our own. Understanding past influences is not always necessary to making changes in the present but can help reveal unconscious patterns and assist a leader in the kind of self-knowledge that creates lasting change. In coaching leaders, certain background and family-of-origin dynamics seem to regularly bubble to the top.

Want to know yourself better and how you show up in the world? Consider the following questions:

How did your family manage conflict? How might that relate to how you manage it now?

Are you an introvert or an extrovert? How did that fit into your family?

Were you more of a close or a distant family, and how might that sort of connection show up at work?

_____

_____

_____

_____

_____

_____

_____

_____

_____

_____

_____

_____

_____

_____

_____

Was communication in your family more direct or indirect?

_____

_____

_____

_____

_____

_____

_____

_____

_____

_____

_____

_____

_____

_____

What were the educations and careers of your parents? How might that have influenced who you are and who you want to be?

_____

_____

_____

_____

_____

_____

_____

_____

_____

_____

_____

_____

Were there addictions in your family?

_____

_____

_____

_____

_____

_____

_____

_____

_____

_____

_____

_____

_____

Were there any major illnesses in siblings or parents?

_____
_____
_____
_____
_____
_____
_____
_____
_____
_____
_____
_____

What kinds of boundaries were there in your family? Was it strict or lenient? Did your parents more often say yes or no?

_____
_____
_____
_____
_____
_____
_____
_____
_____
_____
_____
_____
_____

What was your sibling position? Eldest, middle, or youngest? Only?

_____

_____

_____

_____

_____

_____

_____

_____

_____

_____

_____

_____

Reflect on how your family dynamics play out in your professional life.

_____

_____

_____

_____

_____

_____

_____

_____

_____

_____

_____

_____

_____

_____

Listening to Your Gut

INNER FEELING:

I've been tense all week. This feels awful.

THOUGHT:

I have got to talk to my boss about my workload. It's totally unreasonable and I can't keep up. I have to let him know and ask for a reduction.

RATIONALIZATION:

What will talking to him really do? It's probably easier to just suck it up. Maybe I'll just start looking for another job. He'll never change anyway.

Imagine that someone who reports to you had this conversation in their head.

Do you think it demonstrates leadership? Probably not. So, if you're having this same conversation in your head, what kind of self-leader are you proving yourself to be?

Go back to the problem you described at the beginning of this section.

List all the things you do or say to yourself to rationalize away taking action to address it. Are they in conflict with what your gut tells you is right?

_____
_____
_____
_____
_____
_____
_____
_____
_____
_____
_____
_____
_____
_____
_____
_____
_____
_____
_____
_____
_____
_____
_____
_____
_____
_____
_____

Only you can decide to take action and face your problem directly. Most people won't act until they realize that it is their only choice. Once it becomes nonnegotiable, then you know it's time to act.

Alex had believed that he could carry on for some time in his current dynamic with his boss. He thought he had found coping skills. When he did the work to analyze the true effects of the situation, he realized that the dynamic was affecting his job performance and satisfaction, was affecting his team's morale, and was also leaking into his personal life, decreasing his time spent with his family and creating issues in his marriage. For Alex, being a good father and a husband was a nonnegotiable. He decided he had to act.

What are the nonnegotiables for you when it comes to work and avoiding difficult conversations?

Would you choose to act if the problem adversely affected your health? Your relationships? Your self-esteem? Your career trajectory? List your nonnegotiables below.

Go back to the Feelings Chart and look at what you circled.

Write below all the ways this problem is impacting you and those around you right now. Do any of those intersect with your nonnegotiables?

_____

_____

_____

_____

_____

_____

_____

_____

_____

_____

_____

_____

_____

_____

_____

_____

_____

_____

_____

_____

_____

_____

_____

_____

_____

_____

Asking yourself these clarifying questions can help you decide if it's time to act. Answer each question below:

If I don't have the conversation, how will I feel?

_____

_____

_____

_____

_____

_____

_____

_____

_____

_____

Is there something in particular I want from this conversation? Do I think I will get it?

_____

_____

_____

_____

_____

_____

_____

_____

_____

_____

Even if I don't get that concrete result, is it important to my values to have the conversation?

Do I need to have it in order to act authentically? Do I need to have it in order to support another person? Is it imperative in order to behave according to my ethics?

*WHAT IT IS YOU
REALLY BELIEVE?*

*WHAT IS IT YOU
REALLY WANT?*

*WHAT ARE YOU
HERE TO DO?*

Imagine a moment in time when you were doing your best work.

Describe the moment in detail: Who is there? What exactly are you are doing? Why are you are doing it? While you're working, what feelings are you experiencing? What makes this moment meaningful?

_____

_____

_____

_____

_____

_____

_____

_____

_____

_____

_____

_____

_____

_____

_____

_____

_____

_____

_____

_____

_____

_____

_____

_____

_____

Now investigate a bit more about what made that moment meaningful at the time.

Why did it matter to you? What positive difference did it make? With this moment in mind, what behaviors were you exhibiting?

One of the keys to understanding who we are is to understand why we do what we do.

This question is difficult to answer, but incredibly important to how we live our lives. When we know our motivation for doing things, we are more likely to wake up eager to enter the day. We make a bigger impact with our time and can make stronger connections with others. We make decisions more quickly and with more clarity when we know what motivates us.

To start finding our why, we might consider these two things:

1. **Our strengths:** What are you naturally good at? What comes easily to you? If you aren't sure, you can also ask friends, family, and/or colleagues for what they see as your strengths.
2. **Our values:** What matters to you? What is most important?

For example, one of my strengths is that I am and have always been a very curious person. I probably wouldn't be very happy in a job that didn't allow me to use that tendency.

One of my values is that I believe we should hear from many voices. If I am helping to support that value in my work, I am likely to feel strongly motivated to do `my best work each day.

Looking carefully at these two aspects of ourselves, strengths and values, is the beginning of figuring out our motivations.

Reflect on your strengths.

_____

_____

_____

_____

_____

_____

_____

_____

_____

_____

_____

Reflect on your values.

_____

_____

_____

_____

_____

_____

_____

_____

_____

_____

_____

_____

Look back at your reflection on a time you were doing your best work or felt like your best self.

What were you bringing to that moment? What was the "why" involved?

_____

_____

_____

_____

_____

_____

_____

_____

_____

_____

_____

_____

_____

_____

_____

_____

_____

_____

_____

_____

_____

_____

Asking these questions is the start of finding the why. Usually, our deeper motivation lies below our first answers. For example, I know I want voices to be heard, but if I look deeper, I can ask, why do I want that? Was there a time in my life when I didn't feel heard? Was I affected by someone else's experience of not being heard?

What is it that's holding you back, personally and professionally?

What's the barrier?

_____

_____

_____

_____

_____

_____

_____

_____

_____

_____

_____

Is this an internal barrier or external? Or both?

_____

_____

_____

_____

_____

_____

_____

_____

_____

_____

_____

_____

If it's an internal barrier, can you trace it back and identify where it comes from in your life story?

_____

_____

_____

_____

_____

_____

_____

_____

_____

_____

_____

Whether it's internal or external, what is one thing can you do to move it out of the way?

_____

_____

_____

_____

_____

_____

_____

_____

_____

_____

_____

_____

_____

Lead by Knowing Yourself

If there is one ability that is important for all truly effective leaders, I believe it can be found in an ancient Greek aphorism: **Know thyself.**

It is only when you know who you are, your beliefs, your values, and how you want to show up in the world that you are able to have conversations that matter—the heart of great leadership.

Ask: What is it I truly believe? What is it I really want? What is it I am here to do?

Lead from the answers.

SHARING YOUR AUTHENTIC SELF GRACEFULLY

Our intentions are invisible. People only see behavior. This accounts for many of the gaps we experience between how we see ourselves and how the world sees us.

Ellen's well-appointed office reflects her financial success but also contains no family photos, pet pictures, or anything that hints at a personality. Ellen is stunningly brilliant, entirely practical, and has no time for "warm touches" that don't help her find a cure or save lives. While she doesn't intend to be mean, her chilly and dismissive style has employees complaining. Even the CEO and CFO avoid contact with her.

There are many different ways of being smart. Many people—often the ones we think of as the smartest—don't always succeed in connecting with other people. We *all* have blind spots, and we all have challenges as we learn how best to communicate with others.

Can you think of ways in which your intentions are not matching up with your behaviors?

If someone polled your coworkers anonymously and asked what you were like, what would they say?

_____

_____

_____

_____

_____

_____

_____

_____

_____

_____

If someone asked your close family members to describe you—and to be honest!—what would they respond?

_____

_____

_____

_____

_____

_____

_____

_____

_____

_____

_____

Some people project warmth without effort and understand intuitively how to connect with others. While there can be other sides to connecting easily with others, such as shallowness—sociopaths can be charming, smooth talkers!—overall, sociability is a coveted strength.

Thinking of warmth or coolness as a temperature scale, where do you fall on the thermometer?

Describe two incidents or anecdotes that reflect back this assessment of yourself.

_____

_____

_____

_____

_____

_____

_____

_____

_____

_____

_____

_____

_____

_____

_____

_____

_____

_____

_____

Most people fall lower on the temperature scale than they think they do.

Detail below whether you think that could that be true for you.

_____

_____

_____

_____

_____

_____

_____

_____

_____

_____

_____

_____

_____

_____

_____

_____

_____

_____

_____

_____

_____

_____

_____

_____

_____

When Ellen was approached with honest feedback from her coworkers, she was devastated. Her arms were folded as she read the assessment, and she winced in spots. "I had no idea I came across this way," she said. "I really care about people, and that person they describe is nothing like who I want to be."

The way to influence and lead begins with warmth. Warmth facilitates trust, communication, and absorption of ideas. Warmth demonstrates that I hear you, I understand you, and I can be trusted. People often choose to lead with competence and not warmth, even though most people want to feel warmth from others.

List 5 methods you use to connect with others and convey warmth:

Behavioral research suggests that while people may comply with the demands of a leader who is not warm, they are less likely to feel motivated to perform well for such a person than for a leader who validates feelings, asks about others, and uses more open gestures.

"Leaders who project strength before establishing trust run the risk of eliciting fear and, along with it, a host of dysfunctional behaviors."

—Harvard Business Review

Do you think you might run a little cooler than is comfortable for your colleagues? If so, there are changes you can make to raise your temp in a way that still feels true to yourself.

Suggestions for Projecting Warmth

Ask warm questions. Make the effort to ask genuine questions about others at work. Ask questions that help you keep up with the lives of colleagues, not only questions driven by business matters.

List 3 questions you might ask colleagues to convey warmth:

Practice careful listening skills. Listen to what is being said and convey support and encouragement rather than receiving information passively or criticizing. Offer suggestions, if it seems appropriate.

Detail one common situation where you might improve your active listening:

Be mindful of body language. Crossing your arms across your chest is a common posture but one that appears closed off. Simply learning to keep your arms at your sides is one way to convey openness. You can also demonstrate empathy through eye contact and tone of voice.

How do you normally sit when engaged in one-on-one conversations? Does your posture convey openness?

Watch your email etiquette. In email correspondence, take a moment to say hello, ask a warm question, or offer a note of appreciation. It's not possible for every email but make it a habit as often as you can.

Are your emails, texts, and IMs simply efficient or do they convey warmth? Describe:

Act both from the heart and the head.

Make a list of behaviors and attributes you think fall under each category, emotional and logical. Do they each show up in your behavior at work?

Focus more on being interested than interesting.

Do you ask people questions and listen to the answers or do you just wait for your turn to talk?

WARM v. COLD QUESTIONING

For some people, like Ellen, thinking in terms of warm questions and comments just doesn't come easily. If that's you, these examples can help with both in-person and email conversations:

COLD	WARM
Did you get the work done?	How did the work go today? What was challenging about today's work? Is there anything I can do to help?
Why was the project late?	What happened with the project timeline? Tell me about the challenges.
I don't agree with the decision or the direction this project is going.	I understand there was a lot of thought that went into the decision, and here is another perspective to consider.
We are in a meeting right now. Can you meet at another time?	Thanks for checking in about getting together. I would like to meet with you. Let's check our calendars to find a time that works.

WARM QUESTIONS AND COMMENTS ABOUT WORK
How did the meeting go last week? I thought you did great in that presentation. Tell me more about how it went. How is the project going? What do you like most about your job or project?

WARM QUESTIONS AND COMMENTS ABOUT LIFE OUTSIDE WORK
How was your weekend? How was your spring break? Tell me about your trip. What was the best part? What is your favorite place to visit? How is your family? What are your kids involved with?

Now try it on your own.

Write 3 common responses you hear (or say) in the workplace that would be considered cold. Then recast them using warm language.

What are 3 more warm questions or comments you might use in your own workplace?

List 3 more personal questions you might ask coworkers to connect with them.

Ellen knew she wanted to change the impact she made, so she thought a lot about what signals she wanted to send. She thought of those like a traffic light. She wanted to send a green signal, because she really wanted to come off as approachable. Sometimes she used another traffic light color, red, to stop herself when she was writing about sticky topics, giving herself time to think about how she could warm up her writing to better make her point. She even thanked coworkers for their honest feedback and asked them to let her know if she was coming across as too brash, abrupt, or distant.

What behaviors would you "green light" for yourself?

When would it help to stop a minute before responding to ensure your behavior matches your intentions?

SKILLS FOR CLEAR COMMUNICATION

SENDER

Share INTENT ("Why it is important for me to tell you this.")

Ask for IMPACT ("How does it feel to hear this?")

LISTEN

 **RECEIVER**

LISTEN

PARAPHRASE ("This is what I heard you say . . .")

SHARE what you heard "between the lines"

Share IMPACT ("I feel . . . to be hearing this from you.")

Often we assume that our intentions are obvious to other people. We also assume that the impact we think we are having on others is the actual impact we are having on others. Frequently, we are wrong in our assumptions. By making each of these explicit, we can reduce tension and improve the clarity and effectiveness of our communication. Practice sharing your intentions (why you are sharing this information) and the impact another person has had on you (how you feel or the sense you make of what they have said).

Feedback Survey

If your colleagues can handle the impact, this feedback survey can give you very useful information about your blind spots. Sending your questions by email—with a promise not to get angry at the answers—might make it more likely that you'll get the truth. Just be sure you really *can* accept answers that don't reflect you as you thought you showed up.

The Questions:

1. What are three adjectives that describe me?
2. What do you see are my top strengths?
3. How else could I be more effective as father, sibling, daughter, friend, or colleague?
4. What do you appreciate most about me? Where have I been most valuable to you in our family, friendship, work relationship in the last few years?
5. What was most valuable in the relationship with me ten years ago, and how about now? What has changed or is different?
6. What can I do more of? Less of?
7. In groups, do you see me as a person who asks questions or a person who tells people about things? What's your perception of how I show up in groups?
8. Do you find me direct or indirect? Would it be helpful if I were more direct? Less so? Do you see me as an introvert or an extrovert, or a bit of both?
9. Would you describe me as easy to know or hard to know?
10. Would you say I lead more with strength or warmth, or both?

Then follow up with your work in responding (internally) to the information you receive.

The Follow-Up:

1. Ask yourself these same questions before you read their answers.
2. When you get their replies, can you identify the gaps between how you perceive yourself and how others perceive you?
3. Are there common themes that have emerged from their answers?
4. Take time to reflect on how you want to show up. After reflection, identify a couple of things you can work on toward that goal.
5. Ask yourself, if I had to change one thing about myself in relation to others what would that be?
6. Can you make one specific goal in response to this information for how to better align your behavior with your intentions?

The Questions and *The Follow-Up* are provided again on the next pages with space for your reflection.

The Questions:

What are three adjectives that describe me?

What are my top strengths?

How else could I be more effective as father, sibling, daughter, friend, or colleague?

What do you appreciate most about me? Where have I been most valuable to you in our family, friendship, work relationship in the last few years?

_____
_____
_____
_____
_____
_____
_____
_____
_____
_____
_____

What was most valuable in the relationship with me ten years ago, and how about now? What has changed or is different?

_____
_____
_____
_____
_____
_____
_____
_____
_____
_____
_____
_____
_____

What can I do more of? Less of?

_____

_____

_____

_____

_____

_____

_____

_____

_____

_____

_____

_____

In groups, do you see me as a person who asks questions or a person who tells people about things? What's your perception of how I show up in groups?

_____

_____

_____

_____

_____

_____

_____

_____

_____

_____

_____

_____

_____

_____

Do you find me direct or indirect? Would it be helpful if I were more direct? Less so? Do you see me as an introvert or an extrovert, or a bit of both?

_____

_____

_____

_____

_____

_____

_____

_____

_____

_____

Would you describe me as easy to know or hard to know?

_____

_____

_____

_____

_____

_____

_____

Would you say I lead more with strength or warmth, or both?

_____

_____

_____

_____

_____

_____

_____

The Follow-Up:

Comparing your own answers to *The Questions* with the replies you received, can you identify the gaps between how you perceive yourself and how others perceive you?

_____
_____
_____
_____
_____
_____
_____
_____
_____
_____
_____
_____

Are there common themes that have emerged from their answers?

_____
_____
_____
_____
_____
_____
_____
_____
_____
_____
_____
_____
_____
_____

Take time to reflect on how you want to show up. After reflection, identify a couple of things you can work on toward that goal.

_____

_____

_____

_____

_____

_____

_____

_____

_____

Ask yourself, if I had to change one thing about myself in relation to others what would that be?

_____

_____

_____

_____

_____

_____

_____

_____

Can you make one specific goal in response to this information for how to better align your behavior with your intentions?

_____

_____

_____

_____

_____

TEAMS AND TRIANGLES

Jake is only in his mid-thirties, but already head of marketing for a high-fashion retailer. Jake recently hired Stephen to his team. It hasn't been all smooth sailing for Stephen, though. He's come to Jake several times to complain about the way another team member, Mark, treats him. Because he is their boss and since Stephen is new, Jake decided to talk to Mark on behalf of Stephen. But instead of solving the problem, it only made things worse. Mark is now angry with Stephen for talking to Jake, and the problem behaviors haven't been resolved. As for Jake, he just wants his team to get along.

Most of us have been in Jake's shoes. Maybe we have two friends and, when one complains about another, we take it upon ourselves to let the other friend know there's a problem. Or maybe our mom complains that our brother isn't calling her enough, so we tell our brother to step up to the plate. Triangles like this are common.

FAMILY TRIANGLES ARE COMMON TOO:

Brenda wants her stepdaughter, Gretchen, to check with her before making holiday plans.

Brenda wants Gretchen to change. Instead of talking to her stepdaughter, she decides to go to her husband, James, to complain.

James has a talk with Gretchen to try to solve the problem.

What's wrong with this arrangement?

Most people prefer to scuttle sideways away from conflict like a threatened crab. But allowing triangles to form usually creates new, bigger problems. *X* is disempowered by not having the conversation and stating her truth. For her part, *Y* no longer trusts *X*, because she has gone behind her back to complain. Intentionally or not, the two are more likely than ever to clash. Meanwhile, the third party, James, is taking time out of his day to step into the triangle and setting a precedent for future conflicts.

HOW TRIANGLES WORK

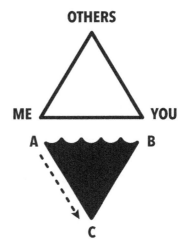

- A & B experience "static" in relationship (frustration, conflict, annoyance, disappointment, etc.)
- A tells C about B
- C is now "triangled" in

Triangles occur when two people experiencing tension or "static" in their relationship deflect their energy to a third person (or thing) rather than dealing directly with one another.

IMPACT ON INDIVIDUALS
- A and C feel closer, and C can feel important or valued
- C can feel distance or a reaction to B from indirect knowledge
- A and B experience short-term decrease in discomfort (because tension is going to C)
- A and B avoid conflict
- A and B develop long-term inefficient and unempowered (but perhaps stable) patterns of functioning
- C feels tension of (or even responsible for) A and B's relationship

IMPACT ON SYSTEM
- Lack of trust (ripple effect)
- Decreased capacity for change
- Inefficient processes
- Norms are developed to support indirect communication

Think through the constellation of relationships you have at home and at work.

Where are you participating in triangles in your life? Describe each in detail. Which part do you play in each triangle?

_____

_____

_____

_____

_____

_____

_____

_____

_____

_____

_____

_____

_____

_____

_____

_____

_____

_____

_____

_____

_____

_____

_____

_____

_____

_____

_____

_____

While social triangles can cause communication problems, there is a human tendency to form them. There are three main reasons for the triangle's workplace appeal:

1. **They are a way to feel like we're accomplishing something.** When we talk to a third person, we get to feel like we're addressing a problem without tackling it head on. If possible, we'd love to never have to talk to our colleague about her annoying emails or the fact that she's slacking off on the current project. Approaching a third party instead is a way to feel we are moving forward with this problem. We may even hope that this third party—especially if it's our boss—will form the third side of the triangle and fix the problem for us!

2. **They feel powerful and/or comforting.** If we are the one who is being approached for help, it may feel good to be confided in and asked for solutions. Or, we may feel a sense of power. Or we could both bond over a common grievance.

3. **They alleviate tension.** Direct conversations can threaten our identity. What if that person doesn't think I'm nice anymore or tells me I'm the one who's wrong, and I have to question my beliefs about myself? Even if you're someone who can handle being direct, you may feel unprepared to manage the feelings of the other person once you tell them how *you* are feeling. Forming a triangle can release this stress and tension.

Go back to one of the triangle relationships you detailed at the beginning of this section.

Identify each participant in the triangle and try to assign one or more of the motivations above to each party. What are you getting out of the triangle? What price are you paying in return?

"Good listening is an excellent trait, but in triangles, what you do after you listen also matters."

- More time and energy spent on negativity than finding and creating solutions
- Focus is on what's not working versus what is working
- Whining and complaining are reinforced with attention
- Battle lines have been drawn, and those on opposite sides view the other as the enemy
- Colleagues bond around their unproductive patterns rather than on their characters, strengths, and talents
- People do not feel valued
- Someone is singled out as the scapegoat and is held responsible for what is wrong in the work environment
- Gossiping occurs

Triangles emerge often, particularly during times of stress or change when people may feel confused or anxious, and they can have serious consequences if they become part of the culture of an organization.

Running through the list on the opposite page, do these symptoms sound familiar?

Detail below the symptoms you recognize and link them to triangles you know exist (or may be a part of).

_____

_____

_____

_____

_____

_____

_____

_____

_____

_____

_____

_____

_____

_____

_____

_____

_____

_____

_____

_____

_____

_____

_____

_____

_____

_____

THE SOLUTION TO TRIANGLES

With some coaching, Jake realized that he should approach Stephen and encourage him to bring his concerns directly to Mark. But it was a conversation he dreaded having. So, instead, he caved and went back to Mark to encourage him to change his behavior toward Stephen. But when he talked with Mark, Mark got defensive, saying to his boss, "Why won't anyone ever just tell me when they have a problem?" The end result: a fractured team.

For most conflicts, the best thing for someone in Jake's shoes to do is to **listen** to Stephen **with empathy and care, help** him **clarify the problem**, and then **point him back** toward Mark **to have a direct conversation**. If employees lack the skills to resolve the situation, it might help for the supervisor to bring them together to initiate the conversation.

If you are in a triangle, **think hard before asking others to intervene on your behalf**. Taking charge of the situation by **being direct**—even if it's uncomfortable in the moment—**will help clear the air** and will **also increase your confidence**.

Jake finally decided to bring Stephen and Mark together for a facilitated conversation. Face to face, each party was allowed to share their feelings and ask for what they needed. The conversation was not easy at first, but with the understanding that everyone has participated in a triangle at one time or another, everyone seemed to take the problem a little less personally.

Think through an issue or relationship that is really bothering you.

Rather than confronting the issue, who did you go to about the issue or problem? What stopped you from going to the person directly to solve the issue?

Choose one of the triangle relationships you described earlier.

What's one thing you can do to break this triangle?

_____

_____

_____

_____

_____

_____

_____

_____

_____

_____

_____

_____

Knowing what you do now, what could you do differently to keep new triangles from forming?

_____

_____

_____

_____

_____

_____

_____

_____

_____

_____

_____

_____

_____

_____

PRINCIPLES OF TRIANGLES

- When a relationship is stuck, there is probably a third person or issue that is involved.
- The third-party acts as a stabilizer for the primary relationship.
- Don't be deceived by a lack of tension. In long-standing triangles, the level of on-going discomfort for A and B may be deceptively low.
- Changing the dynamic means changing our own behavior in relation to the others in the triangle, **not** in changing the behavior of the others.

ARE YOU IN A TRIANGLE?

- When do you go to a third person (or thing)?
- To whom (or what) do you usually go?
- After going to the third party, do you usually go to the person with whom you are experiencing tension?
- What benefit do you get from talking or venting or deflecting to the third party?
- How does the triangle hinder your effectiveness and/or efficiency?
- When are you triangled in by others?
- What can you do to break the triangles in your life?

BLIND SPOTS

Brand = behaviors + results.

Your leadership brand is what people say about you when you're not in the room. Your brand is not based only on tasks or on results, but on your behavior on your way to those results.

Kim, the head of sales at a manufacturing company, seemed to have it all: An Ivy League degree, the persuasive skills of a diplomat, and keen intelligence. So why was she worried she might lose her job? Coworkers had lost their trust in Kim. She would promise to take on a task and never complete it. She blew past deadlines and never took responsibility after the fact. In short, Kim's super-competent, fast-thinking Ivy League brand was not matching her behaviors. Her boss had given her an ultimatum: meet your obligations, or else.

Reflect on your own leadership brand.
Ask yourself:

What do I want my leadership brand to be?

_____

_____

_____

_____

_____

_____

_____

How do I think I'm showing up now? How am I interacting with others?

_____

_____

_____

_____

_____

_____

_____

Am I behaving in a way that is consistent with how I'd like to be seen?

_____

_____

_____

_____

_____

_____

In order to cope with the stress of not meeting her responsibilities, Kim would throw herself into one part of her position, ignoring the fact that anything was going wrong in the rest of her job. This enabled her to keep saying "yes" to requests she couldn't reasonably fulfill. For Kim, this traced back to having to assume a parental role in her family at a very young age. Back then, saying "no" hadn't been an option. Kim's history had led her to being terrified of having open, honest conversations, feeling vulnerable, or asking for any help.

If your leadership brand is inconsistent with what others see, consider why that might be.

Does it stem from a role you assumed in your family? Were there past events at the heart of this disconnect?

_____

_____

_____

_____

_____

_____

_____

_____

_____

_____

_____

_____

_____

_____

_____

_____

_____

Many highly talented, high-performing executives don't always feel secure on the inside.

The inner critic is something most of us carry around. It's that voice that nags you, saying you're not good enough, you're going to be judged, and you should probably just keep quiet right now.

Give your inner critic a name. You can even describe attributes here:

What does your inner critic say to you?

_____

_____

_____

_____

_____

_____

_____

_____

_____

_____

_____

_____

If you had to guess, where do you think the inner critic comes from?

_____

_____

_____

_____

_____

_____

_____

_____

_____

_____

_____

_____

_____

_____

_____

How does the inner critic make you feel? Be specific.

Having divorced yourself from your inner critic, you can work to acknowledge when you hear the inner critic speaking but feel compassion for yourself.

How would it feel to have the courage to be imperfect? To go ahead, take risks, and remain open despite what the inner critic will have to say about it?

What would you do differently if it was okay to be imperfect?

How would you show up?

_____
_____
_____
_____
_____
_____
_____
_____
_____
_____
_____
_____
_____
_____
_____
_____
_____
_____
_____
_____
_____
_____
_____
_____
_____
_____
_____

Describe something your inner critic has beaten you up for.

Does the real you think you have the power to change?

_____

_____

_____

_____

_____

_____

_____

_____

_____

_____

_____

_____

_____

_____

_____

_____

_____

_____

_____

_____

_____

_____

_____

_____

_____

_____

_____

_____

"The difficult thing is that vulnerability is the first thing I look for in you and the last thing I'm willing to show you. In you, it's courage and daring. In me, it's weakness."

–Brené Brown

With their peers, some people are naturally able and willing to be vulnerable and transparent about their thoughts and motives. But for many people, this is difficult.

Do you avoid showing people at work your weaknesses or vulnerability?

How does this affect your performance? Or how does it affect how you connect with people?

_____

_____

_____

_____

_____

_____

_____

_____

_____

_____

_____

_____

_____

_____

_____

_____

_____

_____

_____

_____

_____

_____

_____

_____

_____

_____

_____

_____

What do you think will happen if you show vulnerability?

What do you think will happen if you feel vulnerability?

_____
_____
_____
_____
_____
_____
_____
_____
_____
_____
_____
_____
_____
_____
_____
_____
_____
_____
_____
_____
_____
_____
_____
_____
_____
_____
_____
_____
_____

For some people, being vulnerable with their peers comes naturally. They are transparent about their thoughts and motives. They show up as authentic, imperfect selves, and allow discomfort and uncertainty. Why is this so hard for others to do? One big reason is that we worry about others preying on our vulnerability. We want to protect ourselves, and so we work to appear as if we have all the answers.

Effective leaders have figured out that vulnerability isn't a sign of weakness, but acts more like a superpower, creating strong relationships and solid trust in a way that nothing else can.

Kim was really starting to worry. Her boss had become distant after another incident, this time when she agreed to make changes to a report when she was already overloaded. It didn't get done. Knowing her job was on the line, Kim set about to pay attention to the requests she gets from colleagues and write down how it feels when she responds.

What does it feel like to say no to someone when they ask you for something?

What does it feel like to say yes when you know you probably can't keep up your end of the agreement?

INTERNAL COMPASS

begins with knowing what is going on within ourselves

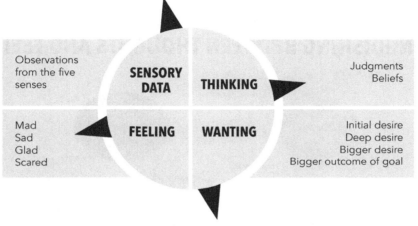

Observations from the five senses	**SENSORY DATA**	**THINKING**	Judgments Beliefs
Mad Sad Glad Scared	**FEELING**	**WANTING**	Initial desire Deep desire Bigger desire Bigger outcome of goal

At any one moment, a person uses four types of information to process what happens internally: sensory data, thinking, feeling, *and* wanting. *Ask yourself questions like these to determine which direction to take:*

What do I think?
What do I feel?
What do I want?
Why is this important to me?
What am I experiencing in myself and noticing in others?
What conversation do I need to have?
What action step is needed to move what I want forward?

FIND OTHERS TO HELP:

Who could I talk to?
Is there a colleague or friend to help hold me accountable?

When an issue is complex or intense, you may have many thoughts about the issue, with one or more feelings associated with each thought. It's easy to confuse a thought that produces a strong feeling with an actual feeling. How do you tell the difference?

DISTINGUISHING BETWEEN THOUGHTS AND FEELINGS

THOUGHTS LOOK LIKE THIS

"I feel like you are not being straight with me."

"I feel like you don't like me."

FEELINGS LOOK LIKE THIS

"I'm worried that you're not being straight with me."

"I feel disconnected from you."

Pay attention during your next moment of stress or try to think back on a recent moment of tension.

How does your body feel? Are you queasy? Is your back hurting? Do you feel sweaty, and is your heart racing?

Now consider your first thought or feeling during that moment of stress.

What was it? Was it a thought? A judgment or other idea? Or was it a feeling?

_____

_____

_____

_____

_____

_____

_____

_____

_____

_____

_____

_____

_____

_____

_____

_____

_____

_____

_____

_____

_____

_____

_____

_____

_____

_____

_____

_____

People tend to identify more with either positive feelings or negative feelings. The more you can identify the range of feelings you are having, the more likely you'll be able to get clear about what you need and want. Below the anger, below the love and joy, what else is really going on inside you?

DELIVER ON YOUR LEADERSHIP BRAND

Kim was committed to change. "I want to send the message that I do care and that I'm honest, even if that causes a little bit of discomfort." So, the next time a colleague asked for something she couldn't do, she pushed back. He wanted it by Friday; she said she'd need until the next week. Was he happy with the push-back? No, but she sat with his displeasure, which was soon replaced by her pleasure in delivering ahead of (her realistic) schedule. She also discovered another coworker had thought she was sabotaging her on purpose—something that couldn't have been further from the truth. Once Kim admitted she couldn't do everything perfectly, connections to coworkers became easier.

We can get so focused on what's important to us that we forget what's important to other people.

What would you want people to say about you when you're not in the room?

_____

_____

_____

_____

_____

_____

_____

_____

_____

_____

_____

What do you think they actually say?

_____

_____

_____

_____

_____

_____

_____

_____

_____

_____

_____

Confronting blind spots happens in two steps. First, you need to identify the feelings you are having. Second, you need to learn the right language for communicating those feelings to others. To begin, it's important to realize the difference between a feeling statement and a thought statement, a judgment and a you-statement.

A feeling statement is the best way to accurately convey your emotions. They are often less hurtful than commands, questions, accusations, or judgements. Simply put, feeling statements explicitly state what the speaker feels.

- I feel disappointed.
- I am furiously angry!
- I'm afraid of moving this quickly.

Take stock of your feelings right now and try to write a feeling statement of your own:

CONVERSATION
In the present moment

PAST ••• **NOW** ••• **FUTURE**

**Conversations
here are about:**

What happened
before (often
based on
recollection)

**Conversations
here are about:**

What is happening
NOW, between you,
me, and the team:

"I" statements **(WHO)**
Specific information **(WHAT)**
Right here **(WHERE)**
Right now **(WHEN)**

**Conversations
here are about:**

What will happen
in the future
(often general
and abstract)

*Conversations in the present are more intense. Though it's easier to talk
about the past and the future, talking about what's happening in the
here and now helps individuals and teams move forward. To spend
more time in the present, ask yourself questions like, "What am I
thinking?"; "What am I observing?"; "What emotion am I experiencing
right now?"; "What exactly are we discussing and what does it mean to
me? to others?"; and "Have I shared 10 percent, 50 percent, 80 percent
of what I think about this issue?"*

In addition to clearly stating your feelings, it's important to communicate about a problem to another person without accusing them of being the cause. They force us to take responsibility for what we're thinking and feeling, which protects others from our blame, guilt and judgment.

The goals of an "I" message are:

- to avoid using you-statements that will escalate the conflict
- to respond in a way that will de-escalate the conflict
- to identify feelings
- to identify behaviors that are causing the conflict
- to take responsibility for resolving the present conflict and/or prevent future conflicts

EXAMPLES OF YOU-STATEMENTS:	EXAMPLES OF I-STATEMENTS:
You should be ashamed.	I feel happy.
You are wrong.	I don't want to do that.
You can do it.	I am feeling frustrated.
You could do better.	I feel confused.
You can't do that.	I want this project.
You are so frustrating.	I feel too afraid.
You make me mad.	
I think that you don't care. (disguised you-statement)	
I feel that you don't want to really be available. (disguised you-statement)	

How to Craft an I–Statement

To create an I-statement, all we need to do is start a sentence with an "I." As simple as that may sound, there is an art to creating effective I-statements.

The basic format goes like this:

"I feel _____#2_____ when _____#3_____, because _____#4_____.

4 Steps to an I-Statement:

1. Use "I"
2. what YOU feel or want
3. the event that evoked your feeling(s) or desire, and
4. the effect the event has on YOU.

Examples:

"I feel (#2) worried when (#3) you are late coming home from work, because (#4) I end up thinking something might have happened to you."

"I want (#2) to have a meeting with you to (#3) clarify this project because (#4) it is important to me that we work on this together."

Situation 1: Mark is frustrated at James because James keeps asking everyone for their input on every detail of his project.

Mark addresses James:

Example:

"You keep asking everyone for all their input on all the details on the project and it's slowing us down."

"I feel confused about the project. I've noticed you are asking everyone for their input on the project. Is there something you are worried about?

Situation 2: Elham heard that Emily changed the project without telling the whole team.

Elham addresses Emily:

"You _____

_____

_____

_____

"I _____

_____

_____

_____

_____

Situation 3: Jack is twenty minutes late for dinner. This is the third time in two weeks and Ethan does not appreciate his tardiness.

Ethan addresses Jack:

"You _____

_____

_____

_____

"I _____

_____

_____

_____

_____

_____

_____

_____

_____

_____

_____

_____

_____

_____

_____

_____

_____

_____

_____

Take what you've learned about yourself and bring it into the world!

What do I think?

_____

_____

_____

_____

_____

What do I feel?

_____

_____

_____

_____

_____

What do I want?

_____

_____

_____

_____

_____

What is important to me?

_____

_____

_____

_____

_____

What am I experiencing—within myself and from others?

_____

_____

_____

_____

_____

_____

What conversations do I need to have?

_____

_____

_____

_____

_____

_____

What action step will help move me forward?

_____

_____

_____

_____

_____

Who can I talk to—a friend, a colleague, a mentor—who can help hold me accountable?

_____

_____

_____

_____

FINDING YOUR VOICE AS AN INTROVERT

Simon is well-respected, likable, handsome...and highly intro-verted. He rose quickly in his career because he is a fantastic thought leader, stacking up accomplishments in his own reserved and quiet way. His company wants to move him into a top execu-tive position, but they aren't sure if he can summon the assertive-ness to really lead. Simon doesn't disagree. Privately, he'd love a job in which meetings held no part. Simon is torn between want-ing to lead and expressing himself authentically as an introvert.

ARE YOU AN ASKER OR A TELLER?

Leaders tend to either "ask" more, "tell" more, or keep their opin-ions to themselves. These differences in personality all have par-ticular strengths but lean too far in any of these directions and problems with connection can occur.

- Leaders who focus solely on connection and ask for rather than offer information can be experienced as too soft, with no backbone.
- Leaders who are always telling and taking strong positions can come across as arrogant know-it-alls.
- Leaders who stay too quiet may seem either overly pliable or distant and arrogant.

Which of these leader types sounds more like you?

In order to achieve more balance, what work do you need to do? Work more on the soft skills of listening, empathy, and storytelling? Push yourself to take a position and share an opinion and idea?

WHAT IS AN INTROVERT?

Introverted individuals tend to
- prefer environments that are quieter and lower-stimulation,
- do much of their best work alone.

These personalities can be misunderstood, particularly in the modern American workplace where communication and assertiveness are often valued as highly or more highly than creativity. Extroverts, who get energy from being around people and communicate more easily, naturally exhibit qualities that are often considered synonymous with leadership qualities.

Does the above description sound like you?

What are the challenges you face as an introverted leader?

_____
_____
_____
_____
_____
_____
_____
_____
_____
_____
_____
_____

Does the above description sound like someone you work with or who works for you?
What challenges might they be experiencing?

_____
_____
_____
_____
_____
_____
_____
_____
_____
_____
_____
_____
_____
_____

Simon knew meetings were necessary, but he hadn't recognized that the moti-vation behind many of these gatherings was the desire for other employees to have time to talk with him and learn from him. Because he would rather glean information from reports or data, he never really understood why people would want more contact with coworkers. Simon came to realize that his more extro-verted peers and direct reports would actually be inspired to work harder if he kept them abreast of his thinking.

Create an Introvert-Friendly Environment

- Provide some quieter spaces for work
- Structure meetings to make sure introverts are invited to share ideas
- Offer multiple opportunities for sharing creative ideas and opinions outside of the meeting environment

Goals for an Introverted Leader

- Practice skills—speaking up, for instance—that are not inherently comfortable
- Plan ahead to meet with peers and direct reports outside of meeting environments
- Find alternate ways to connect, such as writing thank you notes

Extroverts tend to:

- Like to be around people
- Get energy from spending time with others
- Process out-loud versus inwardly
- Act before thinking
- Feel isolated with too much time alone
- Look to others for ideas and inspiration
- Like to communicate by talking versus text or email
- Like to talk about thoughts and feelings

Goals for an Extroverted Leader:

- Sit back and observe before speaking
- Invite others into the conversation
- Ask questions versus telling
- Paraphrase what you've heard others say
- Validate others in what they say
- Ask, what is my role in this meeting?
- Avoid steamrolling ideas
- Create space for silence to allow others to come forward

Is your workplace conducive to both extroverts and introverts?

In what ways? What specific steps could you take to create an introvert-friendly environment?

If you are an introverted leader, what specific steps could you take to connect?

Are there any that you practice now that you find particularly effective?

YOU ARE A LEADER OF OTHERS, AND A LEADER OF YOUR BUSINESS. MOST OF ALL, YOU ARE A LEADER OF YOURSELF. IN EVERY CONVERSATION, IN EVERY RELATIONSHIP, WE ARE ENGAGED WITH OURSELVES AS WELL AS WITH THE OTHER PERSON. THIS IS WHAT MAKES SELF-KNOWLEDGE SO IMPORTANT.

ONE WAY TO LEARN MORE
ABOUT YOURSELF IS TO
SLOW DOWN AND BECOME
ATTUNED TO WHAT YOU ARE
THINKING AND FEELING
RIGHT NOW. *THIS IS HARDER
THAN IT SOUNDS. AS
YOU HAVE THOUGHTS OR
FEELINGS, PAY ATTENTION
TO THOSE, TOO.*

There is nothing more powerful than leading from a place of self-knowledge.

Can you identify and name your thoughts and feelings?

As you do so, you are becoming aware of who you are right now. What are you reacting to? What is preoccupying you? Don't start by judging those things—just become more knowledgeable about who you are.

CREATE A LEADERSHIP STYLE THAT WORKS

Simon was able to make small changes with big impact. First, he set aside time at the end of meetings for questions. Second, he began to reach out to his direct reports for coffee appointments. At those appointments, he could have one-on-one meetings that allowed him to make connections with these important members of his team, and he could do it outside the office and in a controlled amount of time—always important for him. To prepare for large gatherings, Simon made it a ritual to go out for a coffee about an hour before his larger meetings and duck into an adjacent art gallery for quiet reflection.

What situations or environments make you feel at your best, and at what times does it not quite feel like you?

What do you love most about your outside-of-work self? What do you like least?

If you were to integrate the best of both selves, what would that be?

How would you show up more fully? What keeps you from doing that now?

_____

_____

_____

_____

_____

_____

_____

_____

_____

_____

_____

_____

_____

_____

_____

_____

_____

_____

_____

_____

_____

_____

_____

_____

_____

_____

_____

If you were to address it, what could you change or work on?

"You enter the forest
at the darkest point,
where there is no path.

Where there is a way or path,
it is someone else's path.

You are not on your own path.

If you follow someone else's way,
you are not going to realize
your potential."

–Joseph Campbell

Have you ever wrapped up a vacation by losing sleep over the work ahead of you? You might have set aside your cares for a few days, but now your mind is spinning with anxiety about your bulging email inbox, an aggravating situation with a co-worker, or an important presentation. Some of our best vacation moments are when we're living in the now. Our anxiety, on the other hand, is nearly always set in the future—can we handle what's next?

There is a good kind of anxiety that excites and prepares us for something meaningful and challenging. If this is what you feel at the end of vacation, you might feel nervous, but you're ready to stretch your capacity and tackle what's ahead. Then there is the unpleasant anxiety that can twist our stomach in knots, leaving us fearful about the future. It is that kind of anxiety that keeps us awake at night, and that most of us want to learn how to manage.

KEYS TO MANAGING ANXIETY

The first step is usually to take some deep breaths, which helps the body to relax. Then, we can ask ourselves if the anxiety is rooted in a serious problem that really does require a shift in direction, or whether we can manage it on our own.

Maybe you're always anxious about work because it isn't a good situation for you. Or maybe you're not prepared for that presentation, and you need to own up to that fact and reschedule it. Or maybe some really difficult things are going on in your life, and you need to recognize your limits, and reach out for help.

If, on the other hand, the anxiety does feel manageable, it can help to learn its roots. If we can learn about our anxiety, we may be able to honor the discomfort while still moving forward. And this is the critical step: If you can, move forward. Staying still, we amplify the risk in our minds, and minimize our own capacity to be resourceful. Taking action teaches us that our anxious thoughts are impermanent, and we are capable of moving past them.

1. Take some deep breaths, which helps our bodies to relax.
2. Is your anxiety rooted in a serious problem that requires help or is it something you can manage on your own? Write down the issue in detail. Are you unprepared? Maybe you need to recognize your limits

and reach out for help. Or, is this a good challenge? Maybe this is the path that leads you to living in your full potential. Should you seek help or try to manage the situation?

3. If the anxiety does feel manageable, ask yourself these questions:
   - Does it stem from a fear of failure?
   - A wish to be liked?
   - A sense that you are not good enough?

What action can you take to resolve the anxiety?

Did you take action? Write down how it made you feel. Did it allow you to move past your anxious thoughts and feel better?

_____

_____

_____

_____

_____

_____

_____

_____

_____

_____

_____

_____

_____

_____

_____

_____

_____

_____

_____

_____

_____

_____

_____

BUILDING A CULTURE OF TRUST

Monica, the vice president of global marketing at a food industry firm in Los Angeles, is warm and engaging, with an infectious laugh and a fondness for telling a good story. Monica's creative energy and drive had helped her to achieve enormous success in her field. Unfortunately, her drive was matched by an intense need for control. Her direct reports complained she had to have a say in everything they were doing, even though she was too busy to respond with her feedback in time. It had gotten so bad that one of her rising stars was considering moving to another team.

It's not enough for leaders to care, they need to demonstrate that they trust their teams.

TRUST

LOGICAL DEFINITION OF TRUST	EMOTIONAL DEFINITION OF TRUST
"You can predict another's behavior based on past experience. There exists a firm reliance on another's abilities, character, and integrity."	"Someone who trusts a group knows others' intentions are good, does not need to protect themselves against the group, and is confident their vulnerabilities will not be exploited."

Which kind of trust is important to you?

How much do you trust your boss, colleague, or team member? What do you need from others to build trust?

_____

_____

_____

_____

_____

_____

_____

_____

_____

_____

What do you think your direct reports, colleagues, or team members would say about how much you trust them?

_____

_____

_____

_____

_____

_____

_____

_____

_____

_____

_____

Part of why it is so hard for Monica to delegate is that she's the kind of leader called a "doer." She has built her career by stacking up accomplishments, and this was what she valued most in herself at work. For this kind of leader, delegating work to others feels like she isn't doing her job. Monica hadn't yet discovered that an effective leader is not only a doer, but also one who helps others to accomplish and achieve.

CHANGE YOUR FRAME OF REFERENCE FOR SUCCESS

Leadership success doesn't just include doing the work, it also means:

- Choosing the right team, then stepping back and delegating more
- Measuring leadership strength by how happy people are and what kinds of results they are getting
- Creating a culture where direct reports feel safe enough to be who they are and are trusted to make decisions
- Taking pride and gaining a sense of power in helping others shine

Is it hard for you to delegate? If so, why?

In what ways do you actively help others achieve their goals, rather than taking them over?

Review the behaviors in the *change your frame of reference for success* section.

Are these behaviors you demonstrate at work? If not, what's holding you back? What specific steps could you take to build these trusting behaviors into your leadership style?

LEADERSHIP V. MANAGEMENT

LEADERSHIP HAS AN ESSENTIAL FOCUS ON PEOPLE AND HOW THEY CAN BE INFLUENCED		MANAGEMENT FOCUSES ON TASKS AND ACTIVITIES: MONEY, TIME, MATERIALS, PAPERWORK, EQUIPMENT	
Vision	Relationships	Planning	Logistics
Inspiration	Team work	Organizing	Supply chain
Persuasion	Listening	Controlling	Finance/Money mgmt
Motivation	Mentoring	Coordinating	Budgeting
		Directing	Strategy
		Resource use	Decision making
		Time management	Problem solving

It's the difference between directing employees through step-by-step tasks, versus inspiring and motivating them to drive themselves.

It's recognizing that continual improvement and success is achieved in the people and their activities.

It is vital for senior individuals, in positions of great responsibility, to be able to play both roles.

Are you able to differentiate between your managerial side and you as a leader?

Below, write down your leadership responsibilities and goals and your managerial tasks and goals in that area.

_____

_____

_____

_____

_____

_____

_____

_____

_____

_____

_____

_____

_____

_____

_____

_____

_____

_____

_____

_____

_____

_____

_____

_____

_____

_____

Monica's meddling in her team's responsibilities wasn't just affecting them; it was also affecting her own work. She wasn't generating as many creative ideas as she had been before. She was stuck, distracted by managing the team. Monica's team members were capable, proof she didn't need to be overly focused on their work. Instead, Monica was over-functioning as a distraction from the difficult creative work she needed to do.

When we are most successfully managing our lives and relationships with others, we keep our commitments and fulfill our various roles without expecting others to manage our lives for us (under-functioning) or regularly taking over responsibilities that really belong to someone else (over-functioning).

Characteristics of over–functioning:

- Focusing excessively on the problems of others
- Offering frequent advice or help to others
- Taking over the responsibilities of others—whether they want the help or not
- Feeling chronically stressed by these responsibilities and neglecting self-care

Do you over-function in your life?

If so, in which areas? How does over-functioning help you? How does it hurt you? How does it help or hurt others?

Or do you under-function?

If you developed your career as a doer, is that still appropriate to your current role? Or have you moved up to a management role where you need to develop skills in delegating and encouraging leadership from others?

FEELINGS IN THE WORKPLACE

Finally, Helen had enough of Monica's lack of leadership. She quit. Monica's first reaction was to be overwhelmed in processing how to replace her and get done the work left behind. But those were logistics. Behind that were feelings. It took some work and prompting, but Monica finally was able to admit she was hurt. Once she admitted her own feelings, she was able to get to Helen's. Helen had also been hurt and disappointed by Monica's lack of attention and commitment on the one hand and lack of trust on the other.

There's a misconception that we are not allowed to feel in the workplace. But, as we learned earlier, every thought is connected with a feeling, and often our actions—in the workplace and the rest of our lives—are based on these feelings. Even if our feelings aren't named, they are present. When we don't identify them, they can become barriers to progress in the workplace.

Do you know where you fall in your ability to access your feelings?

Do you know how you are currently expressing feelings in the workplace?

_____

_____

_____

_____

_____

_____

_____

_____

_____

_____

_____

_____

_____

_____

_____

_____

_____

_____

_____

_____

_____

_____

_____

_____

_____

_____

_____

_____

Are you aware of the difference between a feeling statement and a judgment, thought, or opinion statement?

Expressing thoughts let's others know what is going on cognitively and what meaning they are making. Thoughts include our judgments and opinions. Try to write an example of each of them here.

_____

_____

_____

_____

_____

_____

_____

_____

_____

_____

_____

_____

_____

_____

_____

_____

_____

_____

_____

_____

_____

_____

_____

_____

_____

_____

_____

_____

Developing Emotional Intelligence means acknowledging that emotions are always present and that doing something intelligent with them is imperative.

Say your boss did not support you in a recent meeting. You might brush it off—he always does that. But behind that is a *feeling*. Did you feel disappointed? Angry? Sad? It's only until you reach clarity about your feelings that you can began to think about what you could do to change your work life for the better.

Recall a recent issue from work where someone did something that you did not like.

What feelings would you use to describe your emotional reaction? Given the feelings it elicited in you, what might you do in response?

Research shows employees value respect from their leaders above all else, yet over half of employees don't feel they get that respect. Full, engaged listening is one way leaders can show respect for others.

The left side of the kanji represents the ear. The right side is you—your attention, your focus, your eyes. In the middle is the heart. If you are listening with your ears, your eyes, and your heart, your employee is more likely to feel that they have your undivided attention and your respect.

Rules of good listening go beyond staying quiet and sometimes repeating back to the other person what we have heard them say and involve having more of a two-way conversation.

Asking good questions by

- Using follow-up questions that solicit new information and demonstrate caring and interest
- Using open-ended questions to help put people at ease
- Thinking about the sequencing of questions to determine whether to start with hard questions or soft questions
- Using a casual tone where possible
- Reading the room and recognizing how the dynamics are affecting responses

Conveying support and encouragement rather than passive reception or criticism

Making suggestions

Do you follow the tenets of good listening above? How might you become a better listener?

Who do you consider a great listener? What behaviors do they exhibit you could emulate?

_____

_____

_____

_____

_____

_____

_____

_____

_____

_____

_____

_____

_____

_____

_____

_____

_____

_____

_____

_____

_____

_____

_____

_____

_____

_____

_____

_____

Monica is learning to slow down and pay attention to her impact. She took time to meet with her team members and offer certain individuals expanded roles. One of the first questions she asks herself in the morning is "What can I delegate?" She's finding pride in being a good leader and in being needed in a different way than before. She is also finding new wellsprings of creativity. Delegation allowed her the time to meet with the executive team and board and to prepare by reflecting on where the company needs to go and researching those ideas.

What would you have time to do if you delegated more work from your plate?

What is possible from the people whose duties you could expand?

_____

_____

_____

_____

_____

_____

_____

_____

_____

_____

_____

_____

_____

_____

_____

_____

_____

_____

_____

_____

Research indicates that putting effort into feeling thankful and, when appropriate, expressing gratitude to others can be beneficial for health and relationships.

Don't underestimate the role of gratitude in improving physical and mental health and in strengthening leadership. Psychologists have been studying the benefits of gratitude, and this subject is also a topic of interest in the workplace as a way to motivate employees and build first-rate teams. While you can't fix all your problems with positive thinking, research indicates that putting effort into feeling thankful and, when appropriate, expressing gratitude to others can be beneficial for health and relationships.

- Thankfulness can help you and your colleagues cope with difficulty and weather stressful times.
- Being thankful is associated with better cardiac health, improved sleep, better mood, reduced fatigue, and less inflammation.
- Gratitude increases your employability. Top employers want hires with strong Emotional Intelligence (EQ).

Praise and thankfulness are motivating and encourage others to act generously.

What are you grateful for?

Living a life of gratitude takes intention. Take a minute to answer these questions right now and focus on the abundance.

What relationships am I thankful for?

_____

_____

_____

_____

_____

_____

_____

_____

_____

_____

_____

_____

What am I taking for granted that, if I stop to think about it, I am grateful for?

_____

_____

_____

_____

_____

_____

_____

_____

_____

_____

_____

How can I be thankful for the challenges that I've experienced? What did I learn from them?

_____
_____
_____
_____
_____
_____
_____
_____

How is my life different today than it was a year ago? How can I be thankful for those changes?

_____
_____
_____
_____
_____
_____
_____
_____

What insights have I gained that I am grateful for?

_____
_____
_____
_____
_____
_____
_____
_____

Who do I appreciate? Why?

_____
_____
_____
_____
_____
_____
_____
_____
_____

What material possessions am I thankful for?

_____
_____
_____
_____
_____
_____
_____
_____
_____

What about my surroundings (home/neighborhood/city/etc.) am I thankful for?

_____
_____
_____
_____
_____
_____
_____
_____

What opportunities do I have that I am thankful for?

_____
_____
_____
_____
_____
_____
_____
_____
_____

Where can I help people more?

_____
_____
_____
_____
_____
_____
_____
_____

How can I say thank you more?

_____
_____
_____
_____
_____
_____
_____
_____

EXECUTIVE PRESENCE

Derek, a big man with gentle features and a quiet manner, loved software engineering in school and still couldn't get enough of it. His management role was bringing far less joy. His team wasn't keeping up, he's been pitching in to help, but can't seem to motivate them to get the work done. Derek is stuck: he wants to command the respect from his team to motivate them to hit their targets, but he doesn't want to sacrifice his nice-guy image.

Being liked can be important for an executive, but it's not news that people who are liked a lot sometimes struggle with being respected. It depends on whether or not the likeable person is willing to take a stand.

"Executive presence" is a phrase used in coaching and in organizations to refer to a quality that is expected of top leaders.

What do you think are the qualities of "executive presence"?

Do you believe you have them? Who in your mind has great executive presence? Describe what you notice about them that you appreciate. What might you want to cultivate more of?

AUTHOR JOHN BEESON DEFINES EXECUTIVE PRESENCE AS "YOUR ABILITY TO PROJECT MATURE SELF-CONFIDENCE, A SENSE THAT YOU CAN TAKE CONTROL OF DIFFICULT, UNPREDICTABLE SITUATIONS; MAKE TOUGH DECISIONS IN A TIMELY WAY, AND HOLD YOUR OWN WITH OTHER TALENTED AND STRONG-WILLED MEMBERS OF THE EXECUTIVE TEAM."

Revisit the qualities you listed on the previous page.

Do yours match up with how Beeson defines executive presence? If not, what are the differences? Do you match up with these qualities as a leader?

_____

_____

_____

_____

_____

_____

_____

_____

_____

_____

_____

_____

_____

_____

_____

_____

_____

_____

_____

_____

_____

_____

_____

_____

_____

THE UNEXPECTED CONSEQUENCES OF NICE

Unsurprisingly, most of Derek's team had nothing but positive things to say about him, except Wendy. Ambitious and energetic, she feels that she and Derek do most of the work on the team. Though she would like to push the others to take on more of their share, she is their peer and she knows she can only push so much. She wants a leader who holds everyone accountable for holding up their end of things.

Think about how the need to be liked plays a role in how you manage conversations and relationships, including work relationships and your relationship with your boss, and ask yourself the questions on the next few pages.

   If you don't feel that being liked plays a role in how you manage conversations and relationships, consider paying attention to how to manage executive presence in a way that is confident and assertive, while also being connected and showing others that you care.

When, in particular, does being liked feel most important or relevant?

If being liked doesn't play a role in how you show up, what ways can you show up that are confident and assertive while also being connected and showing others you care?

In which context or contexts do you tend to hold back inner thoughts? Do you do it most with family, friends, work, team, boss, direct reports, or peers? None? All?

If you were to share more of your inner thoughts, in which contexts does it feel riskier?

What benefits could you imagine from doing this?

How would you show up differently if you had no attachment to being liked?

BOLSTERING YOUR EXECUTIVE PRESENCE

It's not uncommon for very talented leaders to otherwise make excellent contributions to miss out on invitations to the executive team for this one simple fact: lacking executive presence.

In other words, these leaders may have one or more of these characteristics:

- Coming across as "too soft"
- Seeming rigid
- Being emotionally sloppy and leaving resentment in his or her wake
- Having a sloppy physical presence: awkward handshakes, unprofessional attire, unfriendly demeanor

Do you recognize any of these characteristics in yourself?

What changes could you make to move toward greater executive presence that would still feel authentic to you?

ACCOUNTABILITY IN THE WORKPLACE

A lack of accountability is common in workplaces. Instead, people do a lot of hoping. "I hope things will get better," "I hope he will follow through," "I hope no one will notice that I didn't follow through."

The goal in any business culture is to have accountability at several levels—peer, direct report, colleague, and managerial.

- Each individual is doing what they say they will do, acknowledging when they cannot or did not follow through, and holding others to the same standards.
- Leaders also hold direct reports accountable. They must follow through, and if they don't, the leader must be committed to having a conversation about it.
- Personally, each person shows a willingness to own the impact of their actions.

To improve accountability, begin with yourself.

How accountable are you? Think about how accountable you are for your work. Then think about your social impact within the business.

Own the moments when you fall short.

Are you ignoring your commitments because you feel they don't matter? What's in the way of following through on the commitments? After you identify the barriers, what methods can you implement to address those barriers?

_____

_____

_____

_____

_____

_____

_____

_____

_____

_____

_____

_____

_____

_____

_____

_____

_____

_____

_____

_____

_____

_____

_____

_____

_____

_____

_____

_____

LADDER OF ACCOUNTABILITY

Implement Solutions	**INTERDEPENDENCE** • Working with others • More choices
Find & Create Solutions	
Own It & Take a Position	**ACCOUNTABLE BEHAVIOR:** Things happen because of you
Acknowledge Reality	
	INDEPENDENCE
Wait & Hope	
I Can't . . . Excuses	**DEPENDENCE** • Retreating from stress • More long-term anxiety
Blame Others	
Unaware & Deny Situation	**ABDICATING / VICTIM BEHAVIOR:** Things happen to you

When dealing with an issue, figure out your place on the ladder, then evaluate, choose, and act in order to increase your accountability. More people on the top rungs of the ladder means increased chances of success for an organization.

Are you leaving peers or direct reports confused or unhappy because of your actions or the things you say?

_____

_____

_____

_____

_____

_____

_____

_____

_____

_____

SHOW UP AS YOUR FULL SELF

Derek was upset. One member of his team, Sean, was not hitting his deadlines. Wendy was angry with Sean for not doing his part. And now even Wendy, his star, was getting sloppy! Derek was starting to suspect that she was frustrated by the team's performance, maybe even enough to look for another job. Derek knew it was time to act. He committed to advocating for his team more and sharing their wins with his boss on the one hand. He shared his frustration appropriately with individuals who were missing the mark. He also set up feedback timelines, milestones, and other measurements to get his team back on track as well as a mechanism for holding individuals accountable for their work.

What conversation should you be having that you aren't having right now?

Do you do a good job of communicating
the good work you and your team do?
In what ways?

Are you able to hold individuals accountable?

What is the hardest part of that? What would help?

When we stay in inaction, that is our narrative. Taking action, even if it's imperfect, will change your story and build your confidence.

Leaders usually have confidence in some areas of their work life, but almost everyone has times when they feel less confident. Some people feel completely capable of their technical ability but struggle with speaking up in a peer setting. Others love public speaking but struggle with their one-on-one conversations and giving feedback. Some are confident in building relationships, and others are more confident in dictating strategy.

What are your most confident areas?

_____
_____
_____
_____
_____
_____
_____
_____
_____
_____
_____
_____
_____
_____
_____

Where do you lack confidence, or what tasks or requirements make your knees shake?

_____
_____
_____
_____
_____
_____
_____
_____
_____
_____
_____
_____
_____
_____
_____

FOR MOST PEOPLE, IT TAKES URGENCY TO LEAD THEM TO TAKE A LEAP. WHEN WE STAY IN INACTION, THAT IS OUR NARRATIVE. TAKING ACTION, EVEN IF IT'S IMPERFECT, WILL CHANGE YOUR STORY AND BUILD YOUR CONFIDENCE.

What would you do if you were bolder?

If you could let go of some of your fears, how would you show up differently?

See if you can turn the volume down on your inner critic long enough to take a bold step. It could be having an important conversation or taking the first steps to launch a creative idea. A habit of action can help you create a new narrative for your career, for your business, for your life.

What bold step can you take right now?

ONCE YOU'VE STEPPED FORWARD:

Celebrate every win.

Steady yourself if you get knocked down.

Remind yourself of what you believe and what you want to accomplish.

Let bold action be a mantra.

THE CHARACTERISTICS OF GREAT LEADERSHIP:

VULNERABILITY

EMPATHY

ACCOUNTABILITY

CONVERSATION

The etymology of the word "vulnerable" lies in a Latin word, *vulnus*, which means "to wound." To be vulnerable is to allow yourself to be open to the possibility that you'll be touched by the slings and arrows of life and might not come out of every day without some scrapes and scratches—mostly of the emotional or intellectual kind! Just as in love, athletic feats, and great works of art, real success as a leader does not come without taking risks.

Will you commit to the risk of getting to know yourself?

In what ways can you use that self-knowledge to guide your decision-making? Do you commit to following the inner compass, even when it's not convenient?

Great leaders learn to imagine what it is like to be in someone else's shoes. With empathy, a leader can truly connect with the people around them and understand their own impact.

Imagine the person you have the most difficulty with at work.

Can you find a way to empathize with them? How does it change your feelings about them?

You're doing what you've promised and you're following your inner compass, even when it makes for an uncomfortable conversation. You're expecting others to follow through on their commitments, even if it seems easier to let things slide.

Can you commit to holding everyone, including yourself, accountable? What does that look like?

As you learn who you are and how you feel in the moment, you must talk to the people around you. Whether your conversation is more like the one Alex had with his boss, letting him know he feels unhappy and requires a change, or like Kim's, acknowledging her limitations, or like Derek's, as he brings his inner truths out into the open, you will find that taking conversational risks can lead to great rewards.

What conversation have you been putting off having? Can you commit to having it and to sharing your feelings in the moment?

Imagine this conversation and how it will go. How does it feel to work through that scenario? How will you feel after you have it?

"ENJOYMENT PREDICTS
GOAL PERSISTENCE
FAR MORE THAN
DESIRE TO CHANGE."

Much of this workbook is about making changes, with a goal toward sustaining change over the long haul. Experts say you can give yourself the best chance of continuing toward your goals in a few specific ways:

Identify a goal, make it specific, don't make it too big, and write it down.

Studies suggest individuals with clear written goals are significantly more likely to succeed than those without them.

- **Not specific enough:** "I'll lead with more warmth"
- **Specific goal:** "I will take a moment to say hello, ask a personal question, or offer appreciation in at least half of my email correspondence."

_____

_____

_____

_____

_____

_____

_____

_____

_____

_____

_____

_____

_____

Learn how to develop a habit.

According to Charles Duhigg, author of *The Power of Habit*, in order to make behavior habitual you need a **cue** to trigger the behavior, to develop a **routine** in which the behavior is featured, and a **reward** for practicing the behavior.

- **Cue:** Starting a Monday meeting.
- **Routine:** Begin the meeting by having everyone share something from their weekend.
- **Reward:** Smiles, laughter, a more pleasant meeting experience.

Be patient while making a change.

According to several studies, it tends to take around **two months** of practicing a new behavior before that behavior becomes habitual. This suggests that we should put our greatest effort at changing our behavior in the early weeks.

Find activities you enjoy.

University of Chicago researchers found that enjoyment predicts goal persistence far more than desire to change. So, if you are looking for lasting change, find a way to make the change fun. Look for immediate benefits—they can be small—and focus on those rewards.

WHEN PEOPLE FIND A WAY TO SHOW UP WITH THEIR FULL SELVES, THEY FEEL INSPIRED AND MOTIVATED, ENGAGED AND ALIVE.

ABOUT THE AUTHOR

For more than twenty years, Melissa Williams-Gurian has worked as an executive coach and leadership development consultant. Her philosophy is simple: possessing a clear understanding of who you are as a person, which beliefs and values drive your actions, and how you connect with others gives you access to your full potential as a leader.

Her clients include Fortune 1000 companies, CEOs, and high-level executives and their teams from a wide range of fields, including technology, manufacturing, retail, public education, nonprofit, financial services, and health care. She specializes in helping leaders build better relationships, communicate effectively, take decisive action, and recognize and change systemic issues in the workplace. She is also a professional certified executive coach with the International Coach Federation and a licensed mental health counselor who has worked with individuals, couples, and families in private practice.

Williams-Gurian holds a BS from Cornell University and an MA in applied behavioral science from Bastyr University. She lives in Seattle with her husband and three children.

Made in the USA
Monee, IL
24 April 2022

95130836R00122